# OFFICIAL ANNUAL 2022

Tread Octane is raring to go. Match the picture pieces to his car by writing the correct letters in the spaces.

Time to inspect the hot rod's engine. Can you place the gear wheels in the correct order in the sequence below?

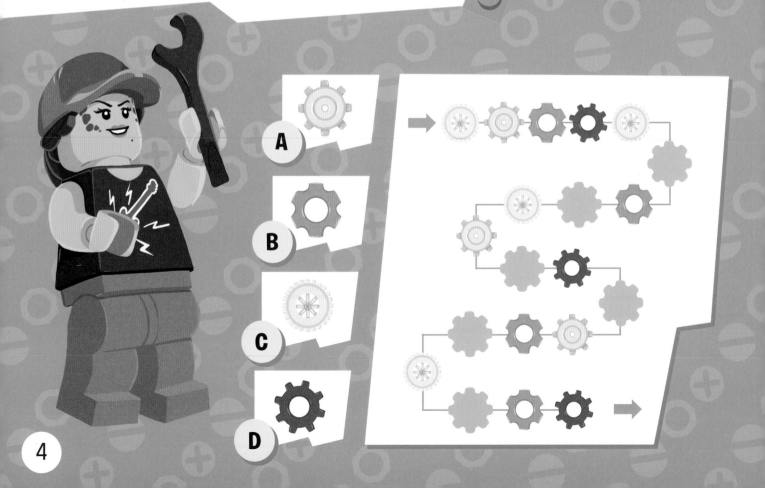

Now test your agility. Draw a path to lead the monster truck from start to finish without touching the sides of the track.

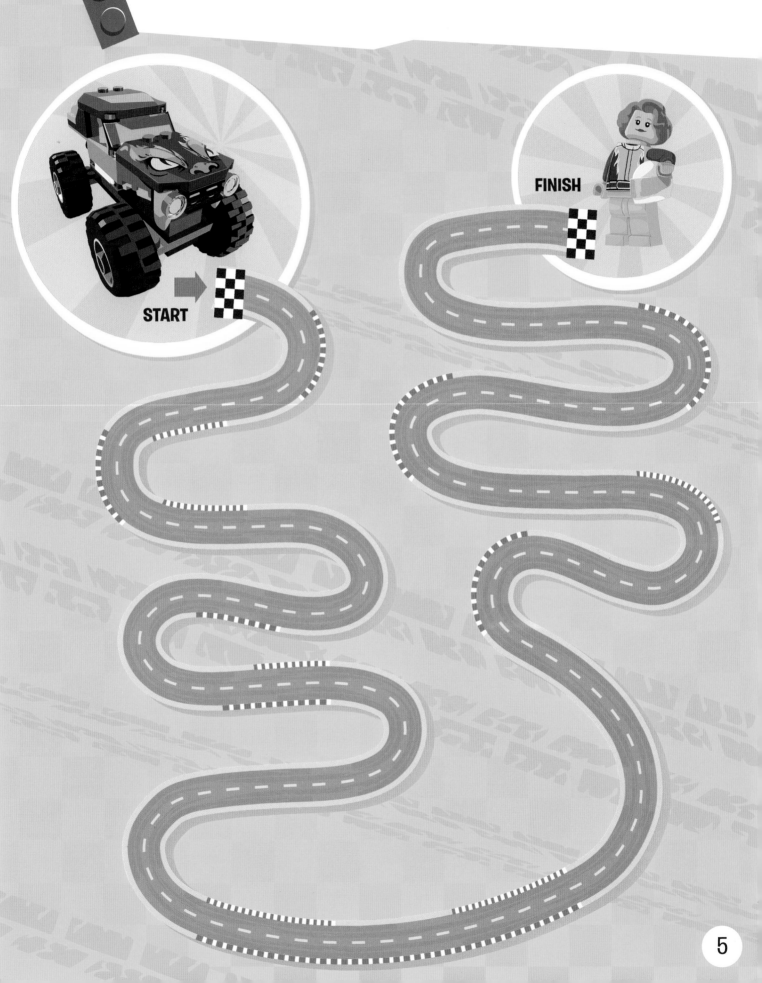

START

FINISH

Amateur racers often build their own speed machines.
Tick the parts that belong to the racing car.

Time to practise some manoeuvres. Using
a pen or pencil, lead each driver along the
dotted paths towards the finish.

Which of the small pictures can be found in the big picture of the monster truck show?

Now that's what I call a monster smash!

Can you work out which set of spare parts matches the engine below?

I love the sound of a running engine!

A

B

C

Finish drawing this picture of a motorcyclist, using the smaller grid to help you.

# UPGRADE

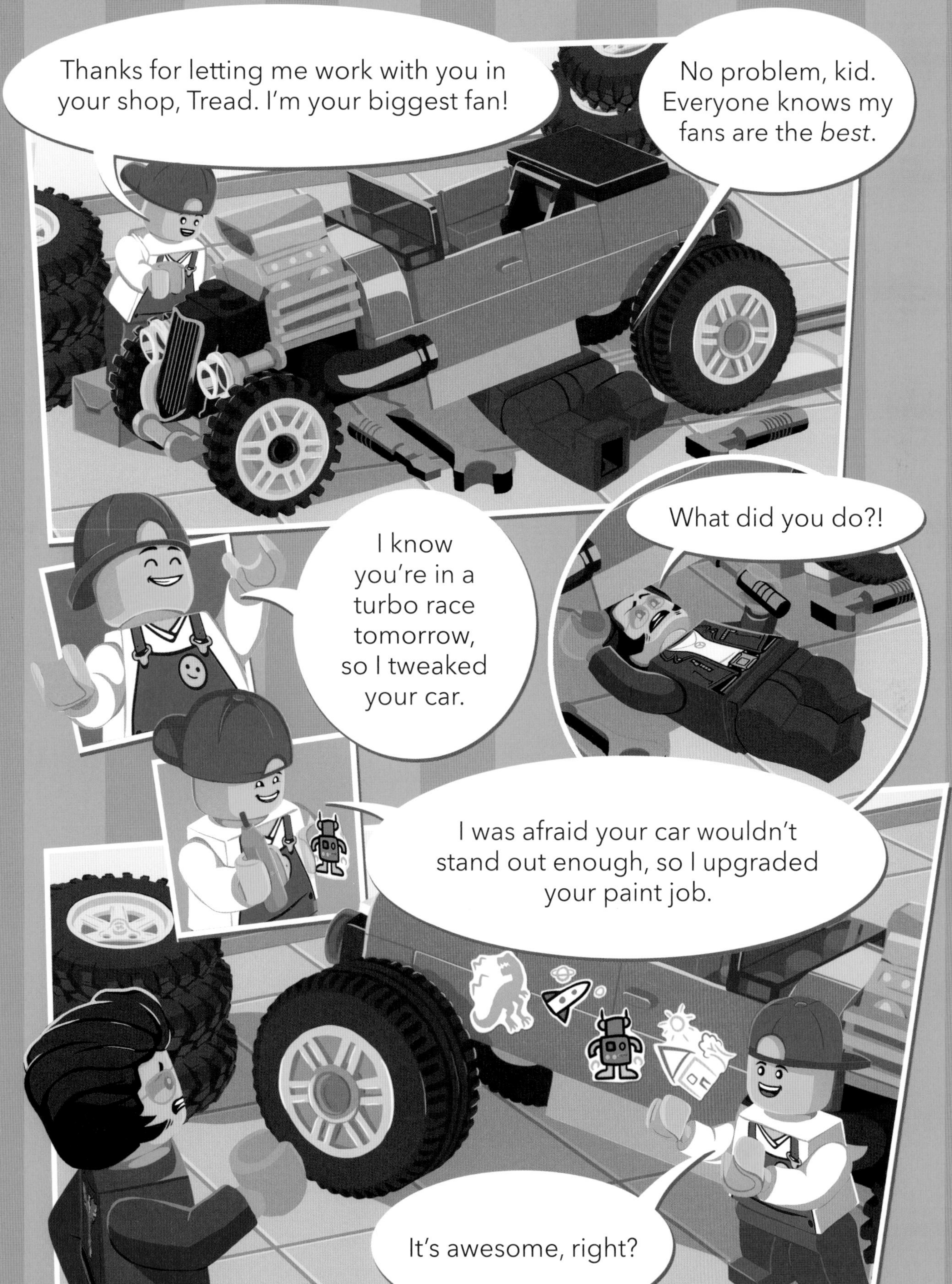

Thanks for letting me work with you in your shop, Tread. I'm your biggest fan!
No problem, kid. Everyone knows my fans are the *best*.
I know you're in a turbo race tomorrow, so I tweaked your car.
What did you do?!
I was afraid your car wouldn't stand out enough, so I upgraded your paint job.
It's awesome, right?

Design a cool outfit and wave-worthy gear for this paddle surfer.

It's hard to find anything in this gamer's messy room! Look at each picture piece below, and see if you can find the ones that appear in the main picture.

I'll tidy up after one more race ... or maybe two.

Tread loves tuning and fixing different vehicles. Help him change the tyres on this racing car. Can you see four identical wheels on the garage floor?

This is wheely tough!

Find three sets of three below. Each set must contain a car, a boat and a helicopter. The first one has been done for you.

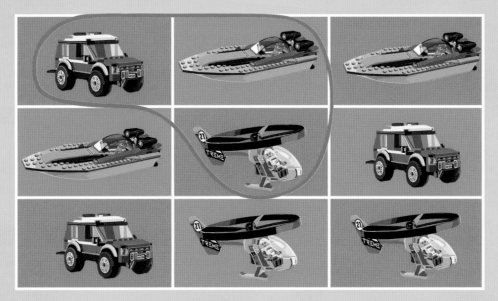

Tread loves to add style to his outfits. Look at his outfits and number them in order of least to most stylish.

You look awesome, Tread!

Untangle the lines to find out who came in first, second and third place in the skate park competition.

Draw straight lines to connect the pairs of identical bricks. The object that isn't crossed by any line is the prize in the skate park competition.

VROOOM! Can you find the brick sets in this racing car's dust cloud?

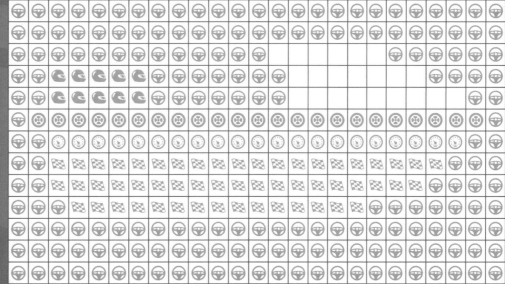

Colour the picture using the code to find out what kind of vehicle Tread Octane is going to use in the next race.

The air show has just started. Join the dots to complete this picture of an aeroplane performing a daring stunt.

Up, up and away!

During the air race, one of the aeroplanes flew into a storm cloud! Help the pilot get through the cloud maze as fast as possible.

It can be hard to see the plane among all those clouds. Which of these shadows matches the picture of the plane above?

A

B

C

D

Read what each character is doing, then use your pen or pencil to draw what you think their face should look like.

**Powering through a long-distance run**

**Busting her trademark trick on the skateboard ramp**

**Getting a flat tyre during the big race**

**Getting a round of applause after her amazing performance**

It's the final stage of the drone piloting competition. Land the drone on the ground by drawing a line along the flight path without touching the edges.

# SCHOOL VISIT

What a tight race! Look closely at the pictures below.
Can you spot eight differences between them?

Which flag should Harl Hubbs wave at the finish line? It's the one that is different from the others.

I hope I pick the right one!

Who won the race? The champion appears in the grid only once.

What an exciting race it was!

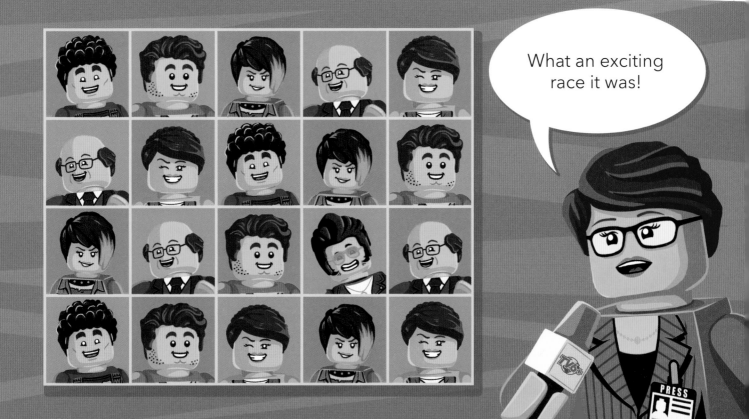

Wow, what a cool trick! Can you work out which reflection is the right one?

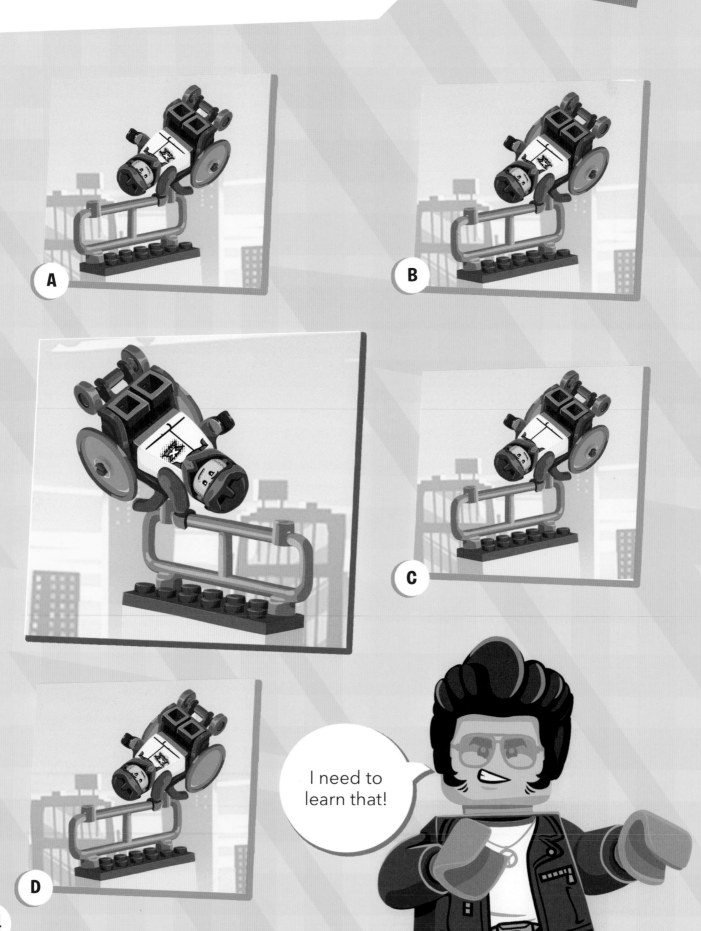

A

B

C

D

I need to learn that!

24

Use pens and pencils to give this skater's new skateboard a cool design.

Can you work out which tracks match the cyclist's tyres?

A

B

C

D

Guide this pilot from start to finish, moving only on squares containing the letter 'F'. You can only move on one square at a time, and can't move diagonally.

START

| E | Y | E | Y | F | V |
|---|---|---|---|---|---|
| V | F | F | F | F | E |
| F | E | F | V | Y | F |
| V | F | F | F | F | F |
| E | E | Y | Y | V | F |
| F | Y | F | E | Y | F |
| F | E | F | F | F | F |
| E | Y | V | F | V | Y |
| F | V | F | F | E | F |

FINISH

26

Colour in the white rugby balls so that each row and column contains one green, one yellow and one red rugby ball.

That looks tricky!

There are always lots of fans at the races. Look closely at the characters below for 15 seconds and then turn the page.

Circle the five characters who were cheering on the drivers on the previous page. Try to do it without flipping back.

This rock star is about to start his show. Which keytar is identical to the one that he is playing?

A

B

C

D

E

Each of these photos from the karaoke contest has one character missing. Can you spot who is missing from each one?

**1**

**2**

**3**

**4**

# RACE & WIN

The annual obstacle race was about to begin. Lots of skilled drivers revved their engines at the starting line, including Tread Octane, who had never lost a race before. VRRROOM! And they were off!

In a matter of seconds, Tread took the lead. "Ha! Piece of cake!" exclaimed Tread.

WHOOSH! As he rounded the first corner, he suddenly felt a strong gust of wind. A newspaper flew right onto his face and blocked his view.

"Arghh, I can't get it off!" shouted Tread. But he was not going to give up. "I know this route by heart. No wind or newspaper will stop me from winning." Even though the newspaper was still blocking his face, Tread drove around the obstacles with ease.

ZOOOP! Tread leapt off the ramp into the air and landed on the track.

SWOOSH! Tread weaved through the cones without knocking down a single one!

ZZZIP! Tread drove through the narrow tunnel as fast as a rocket.

31

Tread Octane was first to cross the finishing line. It wasn't until he stopped that he finally managed to get the newspaper off his face.

"Hooray! Bravo, Tread!" cheered the residents of LEGO® City. "You're the best!"

"Congratulations!" said Mayor Fleck. "You're the only competitor who completed the obstacle course. Your photo will be on the front page of the newspaper tomorrow!" "Awesome!" grinned Tread.

The next morning, Tread bought a copy of the newspaper.

He framed the picture and hung it in his workshop as a memento.

Looking at his collection of photos and trophies, Tread said to himself, "Maybe not the best photo of me, but I'm still undefeated!"

Level up! Move through the hexagons by finding the matching symbol each time. The first one has been done for you.

Let's play!

This rugby player's team just won the match.
Complete his portrait, using the image on the right.

Help the athlete win the city marathon so she can take home the gold! Show her the fastest route to the finish line.

**START**

**FINISH**

LEGO City citizens love racing. Look at the torn picture halves below and pair them up to complete each scene. Colour in the trophies next to them in matching colours to show which halves go together.

Life is a race!

Search Tread's repair shop for the tools shown at the bottom of the page. When you spot them, colour them in to show Tread where they are. Finally, colour in the entire garage!

My garage is my second home.

This stunt show will go down in history! Each of the smaller pictures contains one thing that is different from the big picture. Can you find each difference?

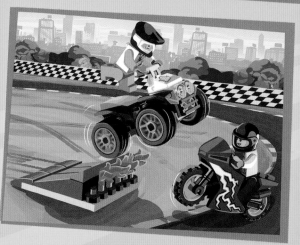

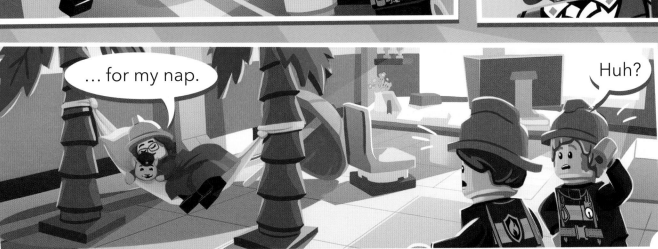

One item in each row does not belong with the others.
Can you spot them?

Time for a tune-up! Match the parts by writing the numbers in the empty circles.

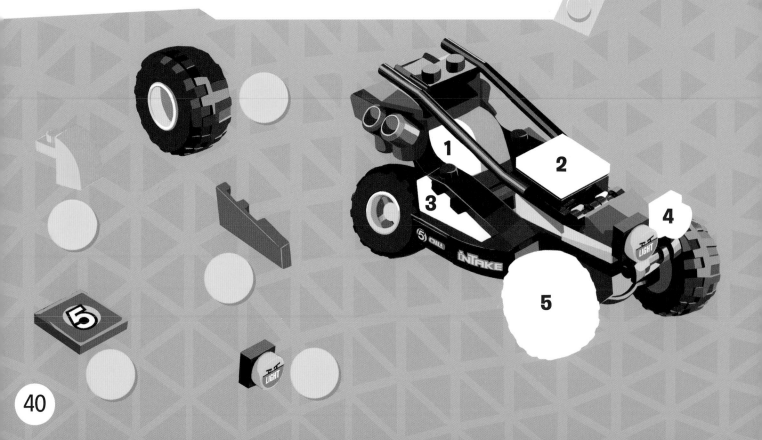

Who will win the junkyard race? Lead the racers through to find out!

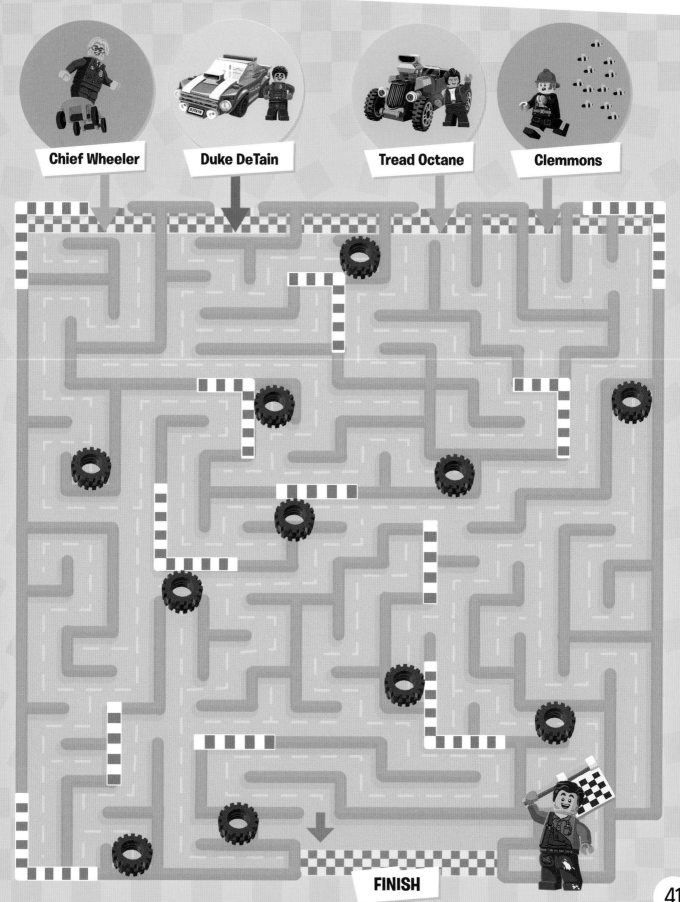

Chief Wheeler

Duke DeTain

Tread Octane

Clemmons

FINISH

This programmer is testing her robot before the competition. See if you can help! How many times does the following sequence appear in the table? Search vertically and horizontally.

**SEQUENCE:**

Take a look at the shields below. Which one looks exactly like the one next to the warrior?

I won the competition for 'best-dressed warrior'!

If you were in a mountain-biking competition, what would your helmet look like? Design it!

It's gotta look awesome!

Match the pieces to the characters by writing the right numbers in the blanks. The person left is the winner of the 'most-awesome-disguise' contest.

# ALL IN A DAY'S WORK

"Special reporter Gabby ToCamera here," says Gabby. "Today I'm joined by Fire Chief Freya McCloud to tell us all about the rescue at the fireworks factory."

"As always, things went like clockwork," says Freya. "The alarm bell rang and everyone in the team knew exactly what to do."

"As we were leaving, I told Bob and Clemmons to fetch everything we needed to get the fire under control."

"Did they manage?" asks Gabby.
"Of course!" smiles Freya.

"What happened next?" asks Gabby.
"My team made it to the fire
in the blink of an eye,
of course!" says Freya.

"I'm impressed," says Gabby.
"My team is the best in the business,"
grins Freya.

"The LEGO City Fire Department is prepared for every situation ..."

"... and we know how to celebrate a job well done, too!" Freya adds with a wink to the camera.

Time for a martial arts competiton. Can you work out which portrait matches the fighter's shadow below?

A

B

C

D

Which of the five characters is missing from each of the circled groups? Add the missing characters' numbers into the white spaces.

Connect the dots to find out which instrument this boy played during the music tournament.

This racetrack is also a maze! Can you help Tread find his way around the track so he can beat his record?

How many times does Tread's hot rod appear among the tangled outlines? Write the number in the circle below.

My hot rod is the fastest car on Earth!

=

# READY FOR ANYTHING

The next day in the park …

Hmm … Where's the starting line?

Another contestant! Tread Octane, why did you decide to take part in a music competition?

Wait … music competition? I thought this was a car race!

No, it's Poppy Starr's music contest! The winner gets to star in Poppy's latest music video.

Challenge accepted! This may not be a car race, but Tread wins every competition. I'll play … the horn!

Didn't I say I win every competition?

This paddle surfer is riding the wave to victory. Which of the shadows below matches the picture?

Surfing is awesome!

Help this officer complete his space-police training. Lead him to the alien as quickly as possible by following the bricks in the order shown.

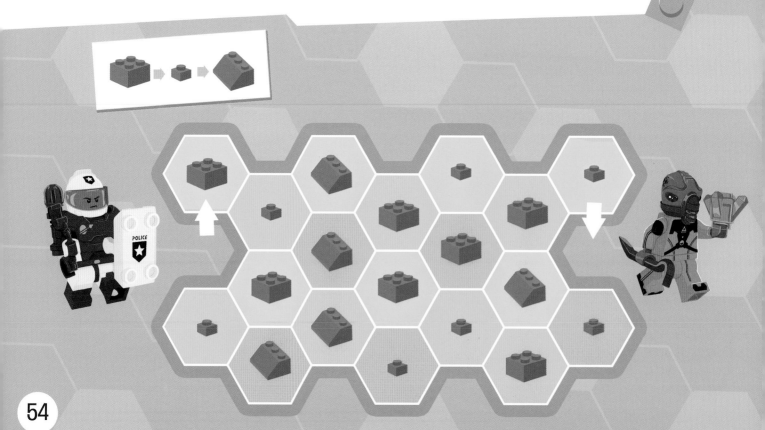

Follow the simple steps to draw your own portrait of this jungle explorer.

LEGO City citizens love races and competitions! How many fans are taking photos of their favourite contestants? Write the number in the empty space.

Only five of these close-ups come from the main picture. Can you find them?

# ANSWERS

p. 4

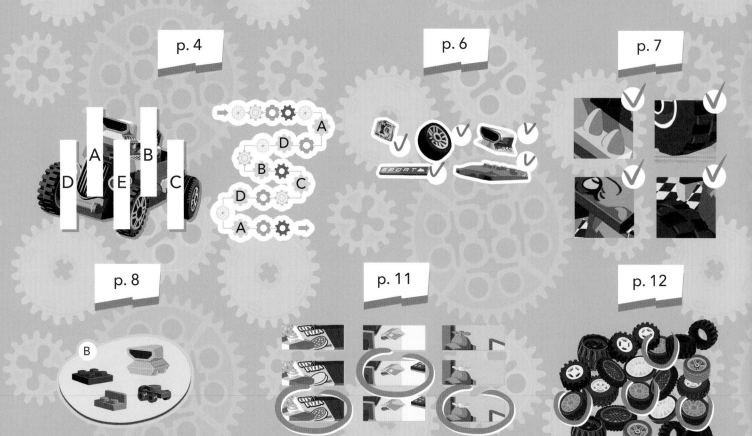

A B C D E

A D B C D A

p. 6

SPORT

p. 7

p. 8

B

p. 11

p. 12

p. 13

4  3
2  1

p. 14

3
2
1

2  1  3

p. 15

p. 16

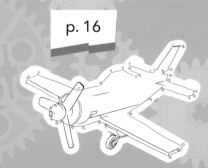

p. 17

B

p. 22

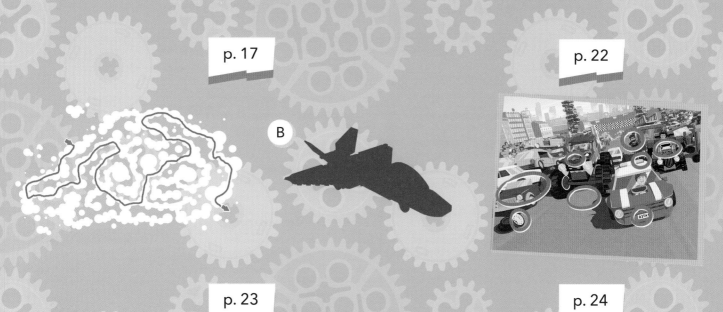

p. 23

p. 24

B

p. 25

p. 26

p. 27

C

| E | Y | E | Y | F | V |
|---|---|---|---|---|---|
| V | F | F | F | F | E |
| F | E | F | V | Y | F |
| V | F | F | F | F | F |
| E | E | Y | V | V | F |
| F | Y | F | E | Y | F |
| F | E | F | F | F | F |
| E | Y | V | F | V | Y |
| F | V | F | F | E | F |

p. 28

p. 29

C

1

2

3

4

p. 34

p. 35

p. 36

p. 37

p. 38

p. 40

5 2

4 1 3

p. 41

Chief Wheeler   Duke DeTain   Tread Octane   Clemmons

FINISH

p. 42

p. 43

p. 48

D

p. 49

3

5

1

p. 49

p. 50

p. 51

= 4

p. 54

B

p. 56-57

= 5

# INSTRUCTIONS